MW00610711

To the one who taught me that love has no boundaries.

—MK

Dear One © copyright 2021 by Michelle Kaisersatt.
All rights reserved. No part of this book may be reproduced in any form whatsoever, by photography or xerography or
by any other means, by broadcast or transmission, by translation into any kind of language, nor by recording electronically or otherwise,
without permission in writing from the author, except by a reviewer, who may quote brief passages in critical articles or reviews.

Edited by Hanna Kjeldbjerg

Photography by Michelle Kaisersatt

ISBN 13: 978-1-64343-823-8
Library of Congress Catalog Number: 2020916341
Printed in Canada
First Printing: 2021
25 24 23 22 21   5 4 3 2 1

Book design and typesetting by Michelle Kaisersatt

FSC
www.fsc.org
MIX
Paper from
responsible sources
FSC® C016245

Beaver's Pond Press
939 Seventh Street West
Saint Paul, MN 55102
(952) 829-8818
www.BeaversPondPress.com

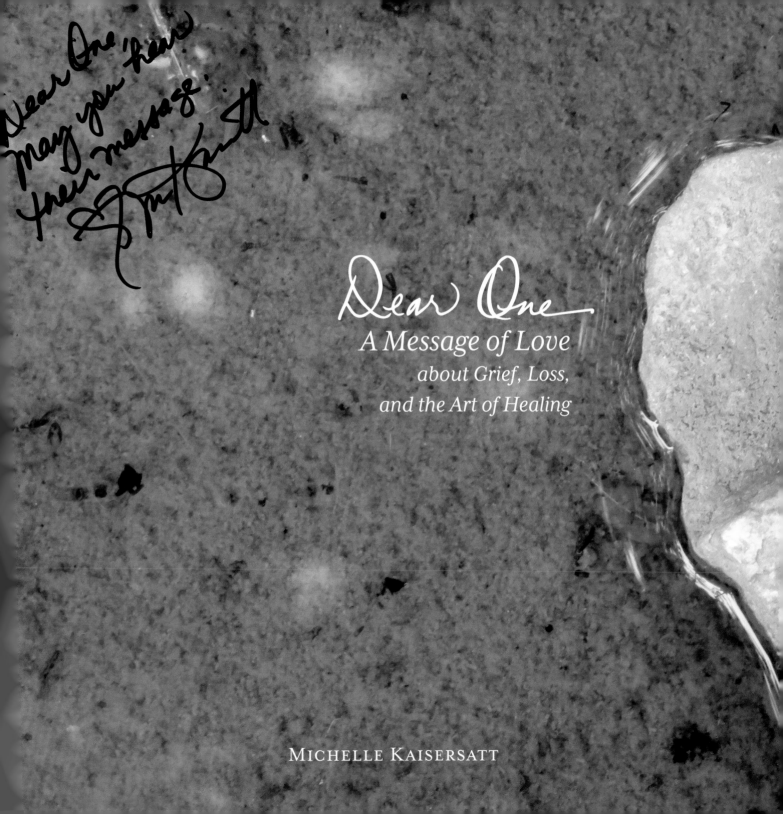

Dear One
A Message of Love
about Grief, Loss,
and the Art of Healing

MICHELLE KAISERSATT

Dear One,
May you hear
their message.
[signature]

Are you looking for me, dear one?

I am.
Where are you?

I'm right here beside you.

But I don't see you.

I'm everywhere!

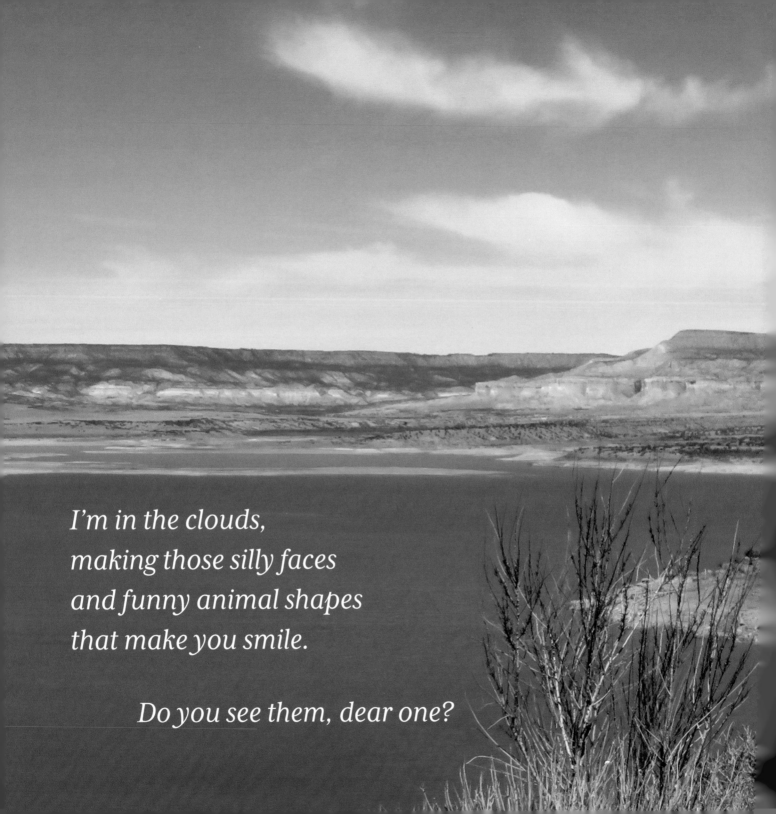

I'm in the clouds,
making those silly faces
and funny animal shapes
that make you smile.

Do you see them, dear one?

Sometimes I see them.

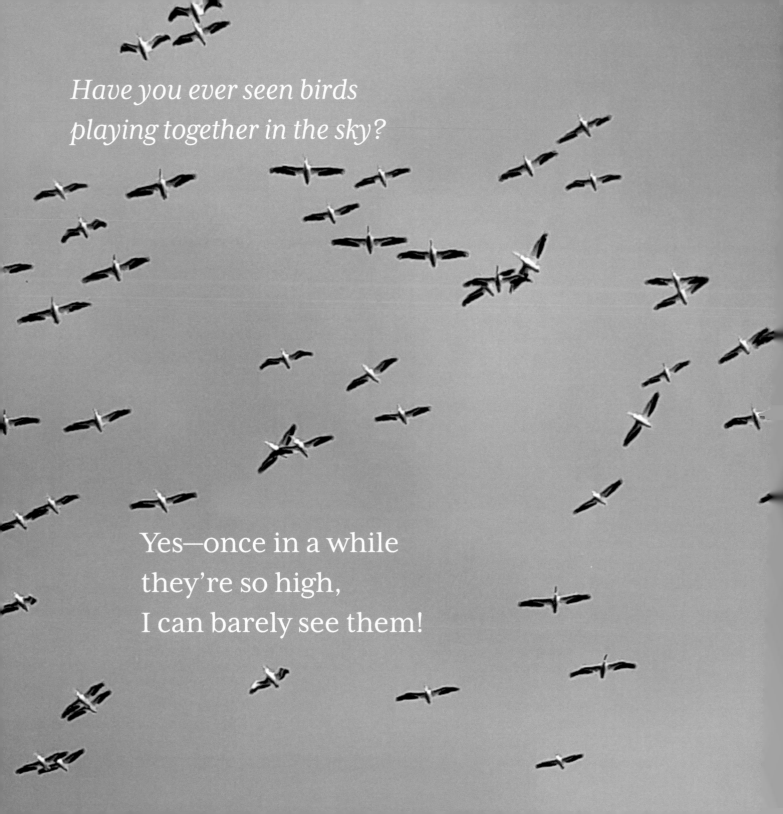

*Have you ever seen birds
playing together in the sky?*

Yes—once in a while
they're so high,
I can barely see them!

*I'm up there
dancing with them.*

Really?

Yes, dear one.

*When it rains, do you feel
the drops as they fall on
your cheek, dear one?*

Yes, I do.

Those are my tears of joy
for all that you are—
patient and kind,
loving and gentle.

Really?

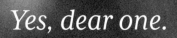

Yes, dear one.

When the sun shines,
do you feel its warmth on your skin, dear one?

Yes.

Now close your eyes.

*Can you feel the warmth of the sun
inside your heart, dear one?*

I feel it.

That's me, filling you with my love.

When you go for walks, do you sometimes look for pretty rocks, dear one?

Yes, I like looking for them.

I sprinkle special treasures
everywhere
for you to find.

Sometimes I even put little pebbles inside your shoes.

Why?

So you know
I am walking with you,
dear one.

When you are really still,
do you ever feel a gentle breeze
against your face?

Yes.

That's when I'm blowing you the most tender kisses, dear one.

I will catch them!

*Do you hear
the birds when
they are singing?*

I do.
But sometimes
it's hard to feel as
cheerful
as their songs.

*I know sometimes
life is hard, dear one.
Think of their singing
as happy music from me.
For I'm cheering you on.
Every day.*

I will.

*When you're on adventures outside,
do you see the beautiful flowers,
dear one?*

Yes.

Sometimes I hide flowers
in surprising places
to remind you to be
bold and free.

I will look for them.

Do you feel the water when it
dances between your toes?

I do.

That's me tickling you—
making you giggle and splash!
May you always be playful,
dear one.

I will.

Many times after a storm,
there are beautiful rainbows.
Sometimes they're even
double-decker special ones!
Do you ever find them?

Yes.

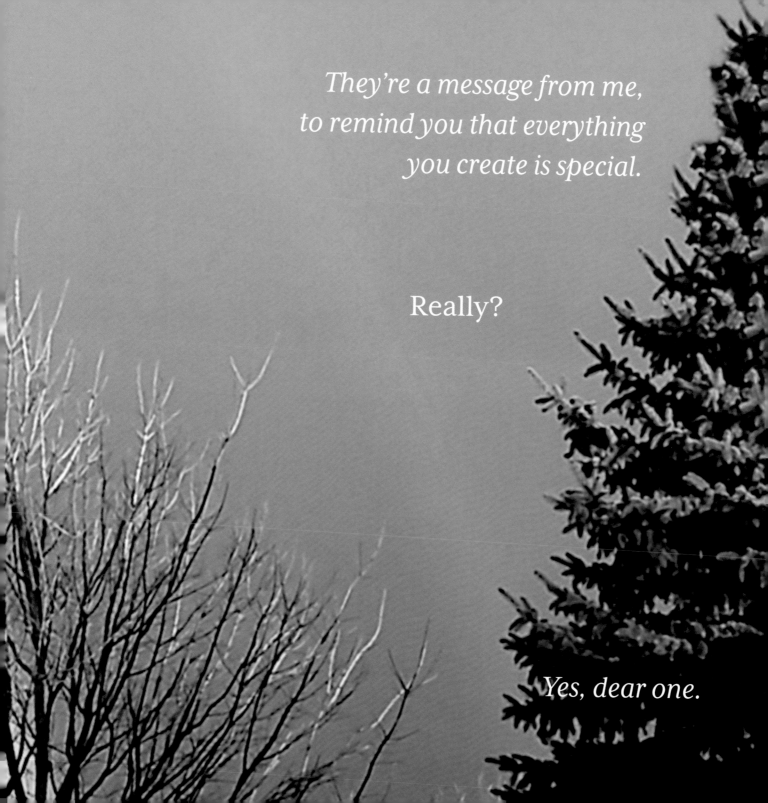

They're a message from me,
to remind you that everything
you create is special.

Really?

Yes, dear one.

Do you hear the frogs croaking and the crickets chirping in the evening?

I do.
Sometimes they're really loud!

We're telling each other about all the good things you bring to the world every day, dear one.

When you look out your window
at nighttime,
do you see the stars
up in the sky?

Yes, I do.

*That's me playing with them,
making them shake and twinkle.*

*Think of them as little sparkles,
lighting your way to peaceful sleep,
dear one.*

I will.

I miss you.

I know, dear one.
And remember,
even when you feel
sad and all alone . . .

I am right here
beside you.

And I will always,
always love you.

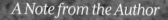

A Note from the Author

Three months after my husband crossed over into
the spiritual world, I ventured back into the world
of the living to help a friend prepare
for her son's wedding. Even though I was in
the midst of grieving, I yearned for the joys in life.

While on my drive home, I needed to pause to
feel all of the emotions in my heart. So I stopped
at one of our favorite parks we had frequented
with our children. Surrounded by towering
trees and a lovely little pond, I set myself down
at a nearby park bench and pulled out my
sketchbook to journal, reflect, and listen
for signs from the "other side."

I looked up into the blue sky, framed by lush
green leaves dappled in sunshine, and
I started a conversation with my late husband,
as I had done many times since his passing.
This book, which intertwines
his words from that day with mine,
has two resounding affirmations:
"I am right here beside you" and
"I will always, always love you."

For those who are grieving and searching for a sign,
it's my hope that this shared dialogue brings to light what
conversation might look like after a loved one has crossed over.

May this book be your guide to connecting with those
on the other side.

May you listen and may you feel their love.

—MK

Reflection Questions

How might your *loved one* connect with you, dear one?

What do you experience that is *unexplainable*?

What *signs* might be your loved one?

What *knowing* have you experienced?

Where do you think your *loved one* is?

Looking back, when have you felt that a loved one
was *reaching out to you* through nature?

What *sign* do you picture yourself appearing as after you cross over?

Do you experience *shivers*? Who were you talking about?

Are there moments when you know someone is connecting
with you from the *other side*? What did you experience?

What song was special to your *loved one*?
How does it make you feel when you hear it now?

᙭

Michelle Kaisersatt is a sculptural clay artist who carves nature and life into stoneware
vessels for the living and into cremation urns for those who have passed. Michelle's work
is infused with a deep respect for how we live, love, and die.

She is a mentor, writer, arts advocate, and nature lover. Kaisersatt's studio, Soul Work, is
nestled along the banks of the Minnesota River in southern Minnesota. Michelle is living
fully by "carving a life"—and is not afraid to talk about "it."

To find out more about how this story came to be, schedule speaking engagements, book
club discussions, and interviews, or to order her book, contact Michelle Kaisersatt at
www.thesoulremains.com.

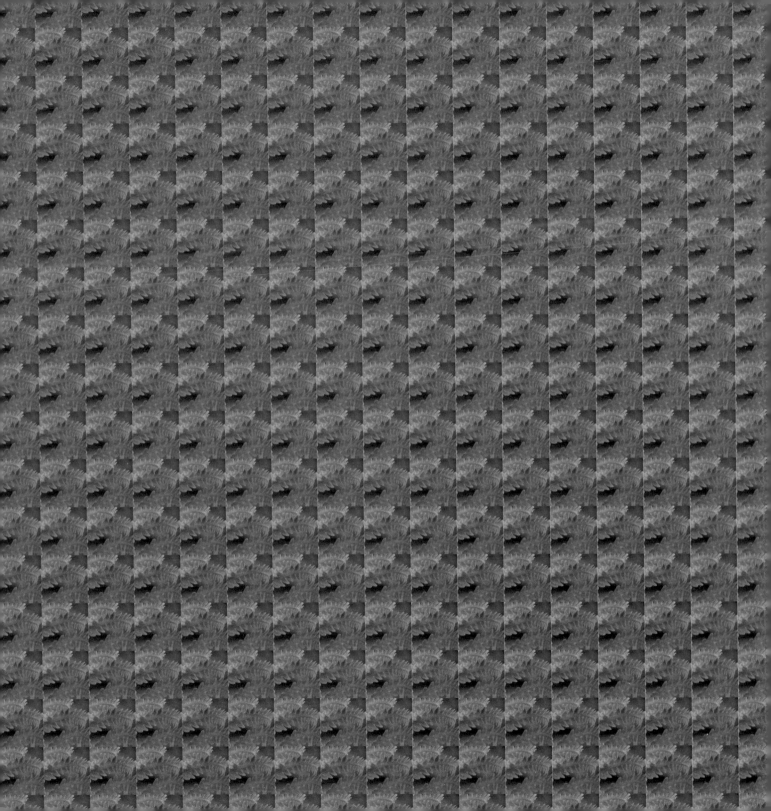